Walt Disney's

Mickey
and the
Beanstalk

 Book One

Disney PRESS

New York

$\mathcal{L}$ONG, LONG AGO, there was a place where the sun shone every day. It was called Happy Valley. Everything there was pretty and green and . . . happy.

High on a hilltop overlooking the valley stood a castle. Inside were many beautiful things, but the most beautiful thing of all was a golden harp. It was no ordinary harp, though. This harp sang sweetly and had the face of an angel. Its magical music cast a spell of peace over Happy Valley.

One day, a mysterious shadow darkened the valley. When it went away, the harp had disappeared.

Without the harp, the magic spell was broken. Soon, the people grew sad and hungry.

Three farmers were sadder and hungrier than anyone else—Farmer Mickey, Farmer Donald, and Farmer Goofy. They only had a slice of bread and a few beans between them. They decided there was nothing left to do but trade their cow for food.

So off Farmer Mickey went. But on his way to the market, Mickey came upon an old man.

"Hello, Farmer Mickey," said the man. "Where are you off to?"

"I'm headed to the market to sell my cow," Mickey explained.

The old man looked at the cow. "I'll give you these magical beans for her. If you plant them under a full moon, they will grow right up to the sky!"

Farmer Mickey was curious, and there was a full moon that night, so he agreed to trade his cow for the beans.

When Mickey returned home, he showed Donald and Goofy the beans.

"Three beans!" his friends cried angrily when Mickey held out his hand. "We can't live on three beans!"

"They are magic beans," Mickey tried to explain. But his friends wouldn't listen.

Donald grabbed the beans and threw them on the ground. They bounced once, twice, and then landed in a hole in the floor.

The three farmers crawled into bed hungrier than ever. They didn't know what they would do.

Then, under the bright moonlight, something strange happened. The beans began to grow. A stem formed and quickly turned into a huge stalk. The beanstalk climbed all the way into the sky, carrying the farmers' little house with it!

When the hungry farmers awoke, they looked out the window. Happy Valley was gone! They were in a strange land on top of the clouds.

Mickey pointed to a giant castle in the distance. "Whoever lives there must have plenty of food. Maybe he'll share."

The three friends ran to the castle. They helped one another climb the stairs and then slid under the door.

When they finally got inside, the three farmers spotted huge bowls and plates filled with food. They had never seen so much to eat in one place!

The farmers ran to the table and started eating everything in sight.

Soon the farmers were too full to eat another bite. Suddenly they heard a tiny voice call out to them from a trunk on the table.

"Who are you?" Mickey asked.

"It is I, the golden harp," said the tiny voice. "A wicked giant stole me and brought me here to sing for him. The sound helps him sleep."

The farmers were frightened when they heard the word "giant." Just then, everything in the room started to shake. Heavy footsteps thundered toward them. A voice roared out, "Fee-fi-fo-fum!"

Mickey, Donald, and Goofy hid behind a sugar bowl. The giant entered the room. He was taller than ten men and looked stronger than forty!

The giant started to make himself a big meal.
As he reached for the sugar, the three friends
scurried to find new hiding spots. Mickey hid
in the bread. But the giant used the bread to make
a sandwich and Mickey got stuck inside! The
giant was about to take a bite when he noticed
the farmer wriggling around.

"Gotcha!" the giant cried, grabbing Mickey.

Then he scooped up Donald and Goofy from their hiding spots and dropped all three into the box where the golden harp was kept. But Mickey managed to escape.

The giant grabbed the harp, locked the box, and slipped the key into his pocket. He did not know that Mickey was free.

The giant sat down on a nearby chair and placed the harp on the table in front of him. The harp sang sweetly and soon lulled him to sleep.

When Mickey heard the giant snoring, he climbed down a piece of thread. Then, ever so carefully, he reached into the giant's pocket and took the key. The giant mumbled something, but he did not wake up.

As quickly as he could, Mickey let his friends out of the box and grabbed the harp. But as they made their way to the front door, the giant opened one eye.

"Come back here!" he roared.

Goofy and Donald ran away with the harp.
Mickey knew he had to distract the giant.

"You can't catch me!" he yelled. The angry
giant ran toward Mickey, who dove under a rug.

"Over here!" Mickey said, but the giant was
not fast enough to catch him.

Mickey ran toward an open window.

"So long!" he cried as he jumped outside and chased after his friends. The giant thundered after him, shouting for the farmers to bring back his harp.

The ground shook with every step the giant took, but the farmers kept going. They climbed down the beanstalk as fast as they could. Donald and Goofy

reached the ground first. While Mickey hurried the rest of the way, his friends grabbed a saw and began to cut down the stem.

But the giant had followed them and was climbing down, down, down. Donald and Goofy kept sawing. At last, the beanstalk began to wobble. Finally it toppled over.

The giant crashed to the ground and was still.

With the giant gone, the farmers took the golden harp back to the castle on the hilltop. Happy Valley was a very cheerful place once more. And no one was more pleased than the three brave friends—Farmer Mickey, Farmer Donald, and Farmer Goofy. They had saved the harp *and* Happy Valley!